D1412634

HABITATS

A Hot Desert Home

M. J. Cosson

Perfection Learning®

Editorial Director: Susan C. Thies
Editor: Mary L. Bush
Design Director: Randy Messer
Book Design: Emily J. Greazel
Cover Design: Michael A. Aspengren

A special thanks to the following for his scientific review of the book:
Paul Pistek, Instructor of Biological Sciences, North Iowa Area Community College

Image credits:
©Steve Bein/CORBIS: p. 6; ©W. Wayne Lockwood, M.D./CORBIS: p. 8 (bottom); ©Kevin Schafer/CORBIS: p. 9 (left); ©David A. Northcott/CORBIS: p. 10; ©Martin Harvey; Gallo Images/CORBIS: p. 11; ©Tom Bean/CORBIS: p. 14 (bottom); ©Richard T. Nowitz/CORBIS: pp. 17, 18 (bottom); ©Peter Johnson/CORBIS: p. 19 (bottom)

©Royalty-Free/CORBIS: p. 19 (top); Corel Professional Photos: back cover, front cover (background, bottom left, bottom center), pp. 13 (top), 14 (top), 15 (bottom), 18 (top), 22; MapArt: p. 5; MapResources: p. 7 (top); Photos.com: front cover (bottom right), pp. 2–3, 4, 7 (bottom), 8 (top), 9 (right), 12, 13 (bottom), 15 (top), 20, 23

Text © 2006 by **Perfection Learning® Corporation**.
All rights reserved. No part of this book may be reproduced, stored in a retrieval system, or transmitted in any form or by any means, electronic, mechanical, photocopying, recording, or otherwise, without prior permission of the publisher. Printed in the United States of America.

For information, contact
Perfection Learning® Corporation
1000 North Second Avenue, P.O. Box 500
Logan, Iowa 51546-0500.
Phone: 1-800-831-4190
Fax: 1-800-543-2745
perfectionlearning.com

1 2 3 4 5 6 PP 10 09 08 07 06 05

Paperback ISBN 0-7891-6625-9
Reinforced Library Binding ISBN 0-7569-4685-9

CONTENTS

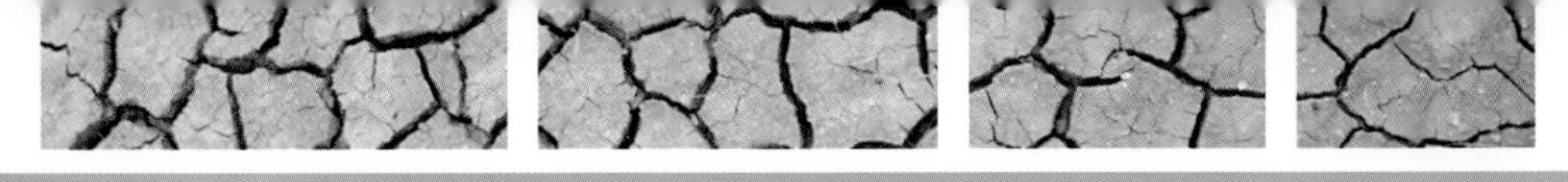

Chapter 1

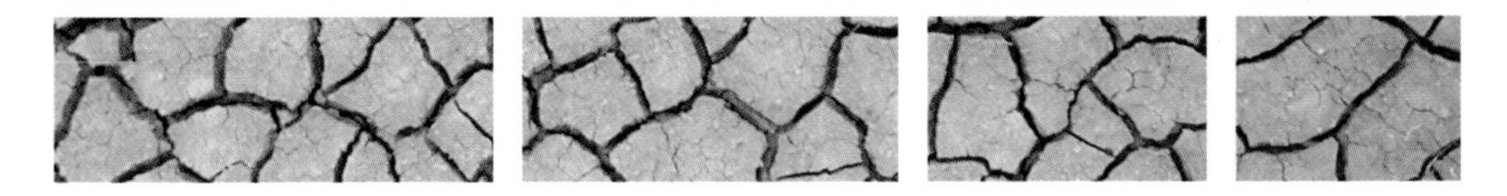

In the Dry Desert

A Desert Description

When you picture a desert, what do you see? Do you see a scorching Sun and endless sand? How about ice and snow? No? Then perhaps you'll be surprised to learn that deserts can match both pictures.

Deserts are often covered with sand, but they can also be covered with rocks, gravel, clay, snow, or ice. Deserts can have mountains, valleys, **mesas**, **sand dunes**, and other landforms. Arroyos and oases are sources of water in the desert. An arroyo is a channel in the desert that is normally dry. When snow melts or rain falls, water may run through an arroyo. An oasis

is a place in a desert where underground water rises to the surface.

There is only one thing that all deserts have in common. To be a desert, an area must receive less than ten inches of snow or rain a year. In other words, being dry is the only characteristic that all deserts share.

The Creation of a Desert

Deserts can be formed in several ways. Subtropical deserts are located near the Tropics of Cancer and Capricorn. Winds near the tropics carry very little moisture, which results in desert lands. Rain shadow deserts sit next to mountains. The mountains block rain clouds from reaching the land. Coastal deserts lie next to oceans. Fog that forms along the coast traps moisture so very little water falls on the land. Other deserts form because they are too far from an ocean. By the time the clouds that form over the water reach these far areas, most of the rain has already fallen.

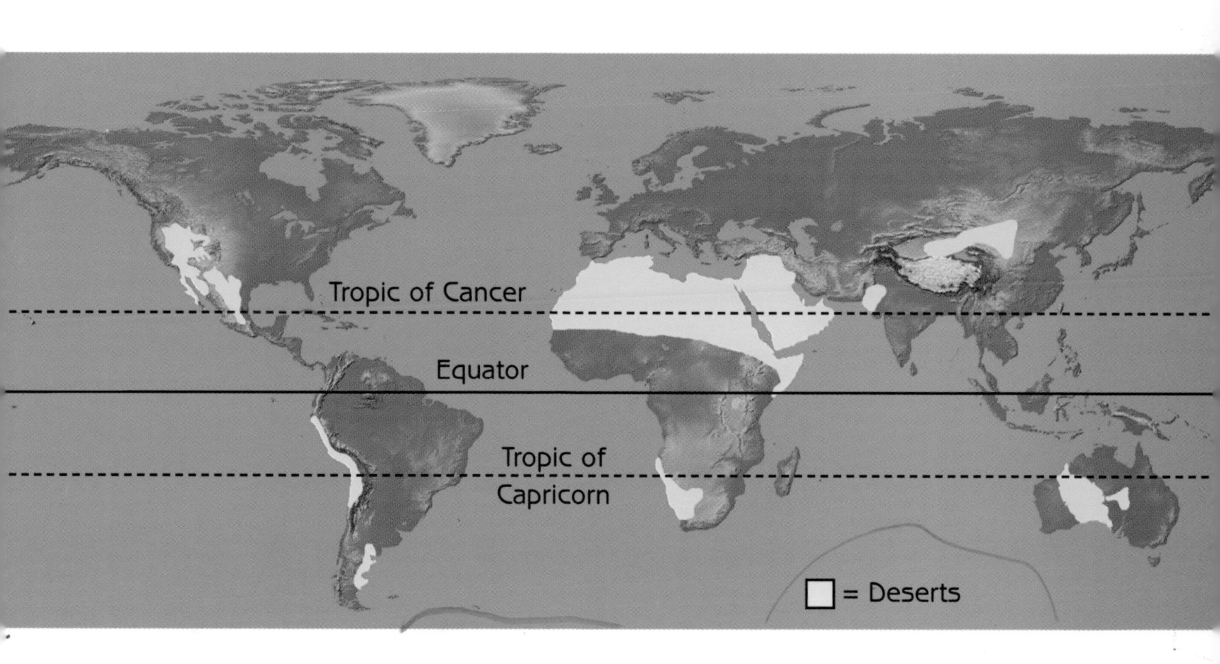

More Than One Kind

Deserts can be cold, hot and cold, or hot. Cold deserts have cold temperatures year-round. Most water falls as snow or ice and stays frozen. Antarctica and Greenland are examples of cold deserts.

Hot and cold deserts are those that have both hot and cold seasons. Often the hot season is very hot and the cold season is very cold. The Namib Desert in Africa and the Gobi Desert in Mongolia are hot and cold deserts.

Hot deserts never escape the heat. Daytime temperatures can reach 100°F or higher. The hot, dry air can make life in the hot desert difficult for plants, animals, and people.

Some Like It Hot

Hot deserts can be found around the world. The largest desert in the world, the Sahara in Africa, is a hot desert. So are three deserts in the southwestern United States—the Chihuahuan, Sonoran, and Mojave Deserts.

Gobi Desert

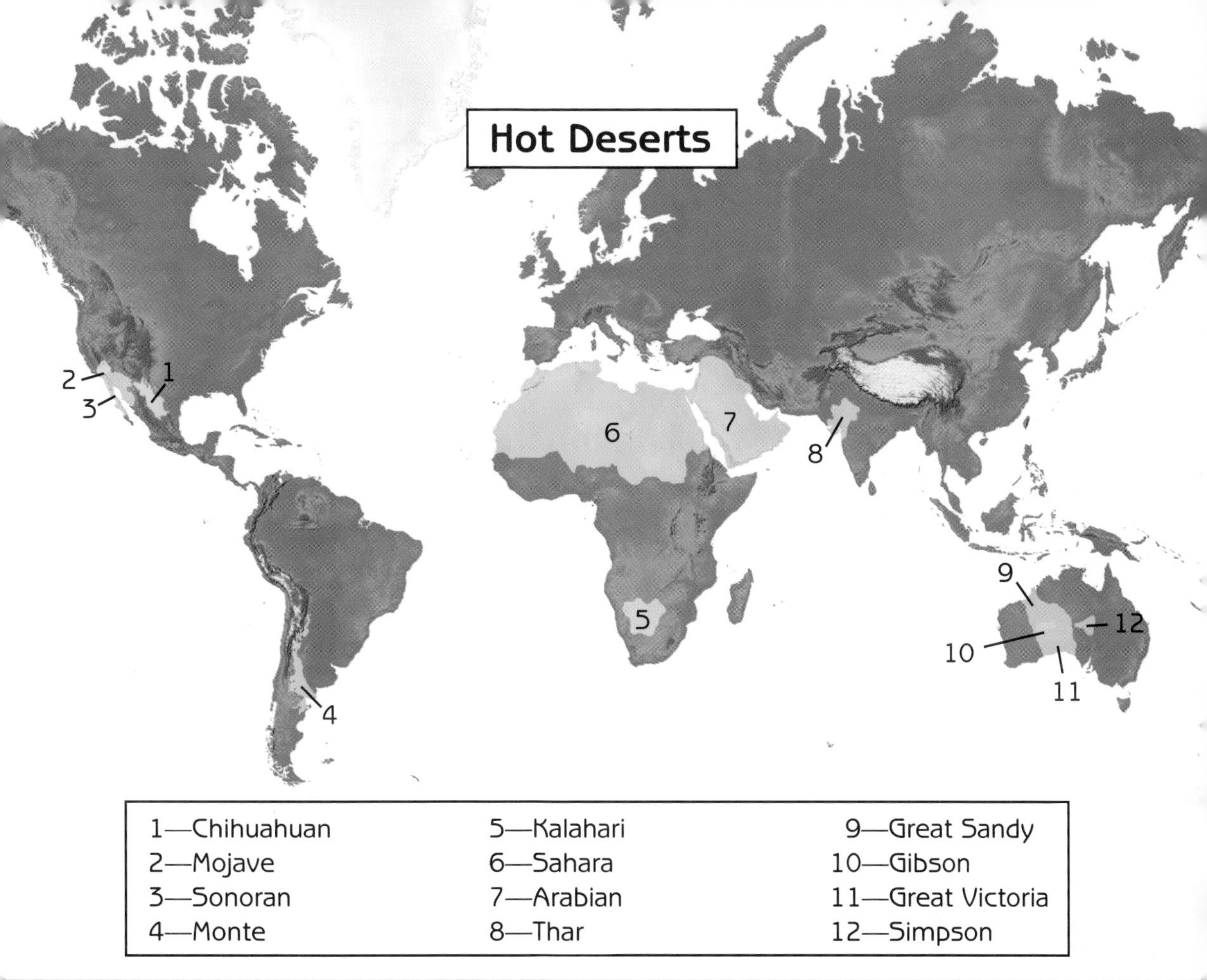

1—Chihuahuan	5—Kalahari	9—Great Sandy
2—Mojave	6—Sahara	10—Gibson
3—Sonoran	7—Arabian	11—Great Victoria
4—Monte	8—Thar	12—Simpson

Desert antelope (also known as oryx)

Hot deserts provide homes for many **organisms**. This home is called a **habitat**. A habitat has to meet all of an organism's needs. It must provide food, water, shelter, and a place for **reproduction**. Let's explore the hot desert habitat.

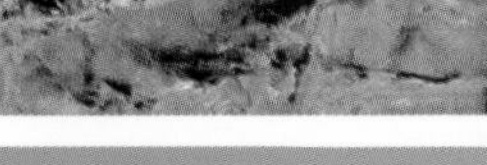
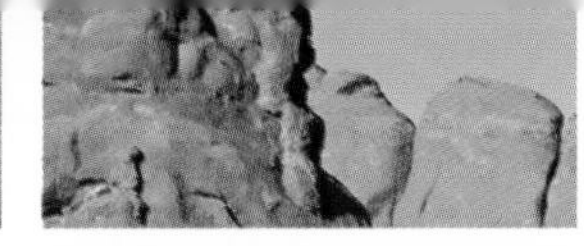

Chapter 2

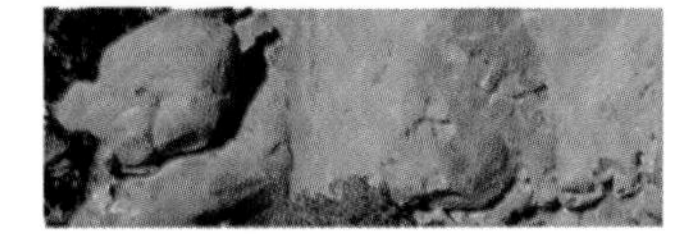
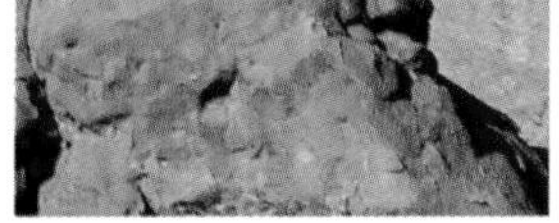

Daytime in the Desert

When the Sun rises in the hot desert, temperatures rise with it. The hot, dry air is stifling. Yet an amazing variety of plants and animals can survive in this harsh environment.

Clever Plants Protect Themselves

Desert plants have many ways of protecting themselves from the heat and lack of water. If desert plants have any leaves at all, they are usually small. This keeps the plant from losing water due to **transpiration**. Desert leaves often have a waxy coating that helps keep water in. The creosote bush is one example of a desert plant that has small, waxy leaves.

The roots of desert plants are designed to pick up any available water. A variety of plants are water seekers. They send long roots deep into the ground to search for water. Yucca plants can have roots that travel as far down as 40 feet. The mesquite tree's roots can reach depths

Creosote bush

of 100 feet. Other plants have wide, shallow roots that stretch out across the surface to collect any moisture there. The saguaro cactus often has roots that cover a distance as large as the height of the cactus.

Cactus plants are especially suited to life in the desert. They have large stems that store water. The barrel cactus, for example, holds water in a barrel-shaped stem. Cactuses also have thorns, spines, or prickles that keep thirsty animals away. The old man cactus is covered in hairy prickles that offer protection. Its white color also reflects sunlight to help keep the cactus cool.

Old man cactus

Agave plants are another type of desert plant that stores water. Agaves have large leaves that take in and hold water. The century plant is a type of agave that blooms only once in a lifetime. This is ideal for desert life, where conditions are not usually favorable for flowering plants.

Agave

Tricky desert plants play hide and seek with the Sun. These plants roll or curl up their leaves to keep them from losing water. This action also protects the leaves from wind and blowing sand. The blades of spinifex grass, for example, are curled to protect the grass in the hot Australian deserts.

Smart Animals Keep Their Cool

A large number of desert animals **burrow** underground to escape the day's heat. Snakes, foxes, **rodents**, skunks, and bats are among these careful creatures. The kangaroo rat seals off the entrance to its den during the day to recycle moisture from its breathing.

The desert tortoise can live where temperatures are more than 140°F! That's because the tortoise spends most of its life in a cool underground **burrow**. The tortoise only leaves its burrow in search of water a few times a year. When it does, it uses its sawlike jaws to cut into tough plants that contain water. The tortoise then stores the water in two sacs in its body.

When food is scarce, some desert animals live off stored fat. Camels store fat in the humps on their backs. They can also drink lots of water at one time and then go days without it. Gila monsters are lizards that depend on stored fat in their bodies and tails.

Gila monster

If you must be out and about, then the shade is the place to be. Jackrabbits rest in shady desert places. These rabbits have large ears that release heat while they're resting. Desert lizards scurry from one shady place to the next. Whiptail lizards, for example, often dart under mesquite and yucca bushes in search of food and shade.

Animals that just can't stand the heat often **estivate** during the hottest time of the year. During estivation, an animal's body slows down and the animal goes into a deep sleep. Estivating animals don't require as much food for energy. They can live off stored fat in their bodies.

Mojave ground squirrels are estivators. These squirrels burrow underground in July or August and estivate until temperatures cool.

Other Survival Tips for the Desert

Camouflage helps various animals hide from desert **predators**. The thorny devil looks scary, but it doesn't like to fight. Instead this spiny lizard changes colors to match its environment. It also looks like a leaf when it moves. The horned toad is actually a lizard with a spiny head and very short tail. Its spotted brown and gray coloring provides the perfect desert camouflage. White Apache pocket mice and bleached earless lizards are two creatures that stay hidden in white desert sand.

It's important to have a varied diet in the desert. Animals that eat only one or two foods may starve when things get tough. The cactus wren eats ants, beetles, grasshoppers, wasps, and sometimes even small lizards. It will also eat seeds and fruit. Roadrunners use their long, thick bills to catch insects, lizards, snakes, small rodents, and other birds. It, too, will eat fruit and seeds. Gila woodpeckers build nests in saguaro cactuses. These birds eat insects, eggs, fruits, and berries.

Thorny devil

Chapter 3

When Darkness Falls

Dusk is a particularly busy time in the desert. Animals that are active during the day begin to settle in for the night. **Nocturnal** animals are just waking. They're hungry and ready to hunt for food.

Plants Prepare for the Day

Certain desert plants wait for cooler night temperatures to begin **photosynthesis**. Cactuses are famous for this. These plants wait until night to exchange oxygen and carbon dioxide. Then when the Sun comes up in the morning, they complete their food-making process. Doing some of the work at night reduces the amount of water lost during hot temperatures.

Active Animals

Nocturnal animals wait for the cool cover of night to become active. A quiet daytime desert can suddenly come to life when night falls.

Jackrabbits hop around, nibbling on shrubs. The eyes at the sides of their heads help them watch for predators such as coyotes, bobcats, foxes, hawks, horned owls, and snakes. If threatened, jackrabbits can take off at speeds of 35 mph or leap 20 feet to escape.

Jackrabbit

Rodents are popular desert dwellers. Kangaroo rats have huge eyes to help them see at night. These small animals hop around like kangaroos. They never drink water. Instead their bodies make water from the seeds they eat. Pack rats have very large eyes too. They scurry about gathering seeds and plants to store.

Creepy, crawly creatures enjoy the nighttime hours too. Desert tarantulas don't spin webs like other spiders. Instead they chase after insects, lizards, and other small animals. Scorpions have stingers with poisonous venom that they use to catch **prey** and to defend themselves. This venom is rarely deadly for humans though.

Scorpion

Tarantula

Sidewinder

The diamondback and sidewinder are two desert rattlesnakes. They may not be seen in the dark, but the rattle on the end of their tails warns nearby animals to stay back. The diamondback gets it name from the gray to brown diamond-shaped spots on its back. While resting during the day, the snake's coloring often serves as camouflage against sand and rock. The sidewinder gets its name from the way it moves in a sideways motion so that only two short sections of the snake touch the hot ground at any time.

Scientist of Significance

Even as a young boy, Laurence Klauber had an interest in snakes. As a young man, he officially began working with snakes when the San Diego Zoo asked him to help identify several varieties. Klauber then spent the next 35 years studying snakes. Much of his research was done in the desert. He found that snakes were more common there than in other environments, especially in the first few weeks of spring.

Klauber's most important contribution was his classification of rattlesnakes. He used math to identify types of rattlers by the pattern and number of their scales. Klauber's book about rattlesnakes is read by serious snake lovers everywhere. He is known around the world as "Mr. Rattlesnake."

Diamondback

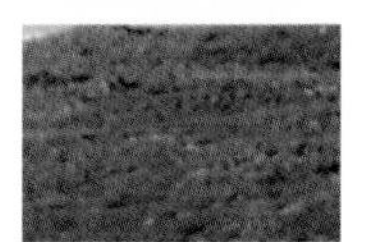

Chapter 4

After the Rain

Rain is scarce in the desert. But after a rare or brief rain, plants and animals come to life.

Plants

After a rain, cactuses gather as much water as possible to store until the next rainfall. Existing roots sprout small rain roots to help absorb more water. When the ground is dry again, the rain roots shrivel and drop off.

Plants that can't handle the dry weather often become **dormant** or die. **Perennials** will either drop their leaves or die back to a **bulb**. New growth will occur as soon as the rain comes again. **Annual** plants die, leaving only their seeds behind. With rain, the seeds of both annuals and perennials will sprout and grow quickly. The desert is suddenly carpeted with beautiful flowers. After a short growing season, the plants either die or go dormant again until the next rain comes.

The verbena is a sticky, hairy plant that doesn't look like much until it rains. When rain does fall, beautiful bright pink flowers appear. Most of the time, the ocotillo plant looks like a bunch of dry sticks. But after a rain, leaves and sometimes red flowers appear. The California poppy, desert dandelion, mallow, desert pea, and evening primrose are other desert flowers that bloom after it rains.

Inquire and Investigate
Desert Flowers in the Rain

Question: What do desert flower seeds need to sprout?

Answer the question: I think the flower seeds need ______________ to sprout.

Form a hypothesis: Flower seeds need ______________ to sprout.

Test the Hypothesis

Materials

- two snack-size baggies
- dry flower seeds
- water
- cookie sheet

Procedure

- Fill both bags with dry seeds. Seal one bag. Pour water into the other bag until it's full. Seal the bag.
- Place both bags on the cookie sheet. Put the sheet in a sunny location. Leave it out for several days to a week. Observe what happens to the seeds in each bag.

Observations: The seeds in the bag with water sprout and may even pop the bag open. The seeds without water don't change.

Conclusions: Flower seeds need water to sprout. In the desert, rain is scarce, so plant seeds have very few opportunities to sprout. But after a rain, many flowering plants burst into life for a short period of time.

Animals

Rain also refreshes desert animals. Desert toads remain dormant deep in the ground until rain comes. After the rain, the toads make their way back to the surface. Here they jump in ponds and puddles and burrow in moist soil.

During a desert rainstorm, tiny brine and fairy shrimp eggs hatch in puddles on the ground. The shrimp lay new eggs before the puddles dry up. The eggs can lie dormant on dry ground for years before their life cycle begins again.

Unlike many desert animals, Bighorn sheep don't have special features for storing water. This means they normally stay close to water sources in the desert. After it rains, however, the sheep can spread out to search for food. Bighorns eat a variety of plants. They will even eat cactuses when that's all that's available. The sheep use their hooves and horns to strip the spines from cactuses. Then they can eat the juicy insides.

Addaxes never drink. They get all their water from the plants they eat. Because of this, addaxes follow the rain because they know that green, leafy plants will appear afterward.

Addax

CHAPTER 5

Desert Dwellers

Imagine living in a land with scorching temperatures and very little water. That's the life of hot desert dwellers.

Nomads

Deserts are home to several groups of nomads. Nomads are people who travel from one place to another. When the water and food in one area are gone, nomads move to another area.

Bedouin is the Arabic word for "desert dweller." The Bedouin people are nomads who herd camels, sheep, and

Bedouin

Aborigine

goats in the Arabian Desert. They live in tents so they can easily move from one location to another.

The Aborigines of the Australian deserts are also nomadic. They hunt with spears made from the acacia tree. Aborigines cook lizards, kangaroos, and **grubs**. They make seedcakes from the seeds of desert plants.

The nomadic San people live in the Kalahari Desert. The San are hunters and gatherers. The men hunt large animals. The women collect edible plants and trap small animals.

San

Native Americans

Native Americans have lived in the hot U.S. deserts for thousands of years. They used desert plants to make necessities. For example, the century plant was used to make soap, food, **fibers**, medicines, and weapons. Many Native American groups were farmers. Some farmed only during periods of rain. Others used **irrigation** methods to bring water to dry land. The Pueblo, Navajo, and Apache are among the Native American groups that still live in hot desert lands today.

Technology Link

Thanks to technology, large cities such as Las Vegas and Phoenix thrive in the desert. The Hoover Dam, located between Nevada and Arizona, was built in the 1930s. The **dam** directs water from the Colorado River to more than 20 million people in California, Arizona, and Nevada. It also provides **hydroelectric** power and water for irrigation.

Dangers to Desert Dwellers

Many people who live in the desert are in danger of losing their homes. As populations grow, the land near deserts is used for farming, grazing, and building houses. This damages the natural desert habitat and changes the boundaries of deserts.

Precious minerals, such as oil and diamonds, have been found under desert lands. When the minerals are removed from an area, plant and animal habitats are destroyed. People are forced off their land.

Deserts may be hot and dry, but they are home to millions of plants, animals, and people. It's important to protect deserts and their inhabitants.

Hoover Dam

INTERNET CONNECTIONS and RELATED READING for the DESERT HABITAT

http://www.desertusa.com/life.html
Check out Desert USA for information on American desert animals, plants, and people.

http://mbgnet.mobot.org/sets/desert/
Take a trip through the desert to learn what it's like there. Meet the plants and animals of this hot habitat.

http://www.enchantedlearning.com/biomes/desert/desert.shtml
This site includes a map of the major deserts, a chart of the animals found in each one, and in-depth information on many desert animals.

http://imagers.gsfc.nasa.gov/fieldguide/
These photo cards provide a picture and brief description of desert plants and animals.

The Desert Alphabet Book by Jerry Pallotta. The parched, mysterious deserts of the world are the landscapes for this alphabetic array of plants, animals, and phenomena. Charlesbridge Press, 1994. [RL 2 IL K–4] (4691201 PB)

Desert Animals at Night by Lynn M. Stone. Describes the behavior of desert animals at night. Rourke Book Company, 1997. [RL 4.3 IL 3–7] (4438701 PB)

The Desert Is Theirs by Byrd Baylor. A lyrical description of the relationship between the desert and the many creatures, including humans, who live there. Macmillan, 1987. [RL 3 IL 1–4] (8675701 PB)

Deserts by Neil Morris. Looks at the various aspects of deserts, including natural features, wildlife, and the effects of humans. Crabtree Publishing, 1996. [RL 4 IL 2–5] (4974301 PB 4974302 CC)

A Walk in the Desert by Rebecca L. Johnson. This book describes the climate, seasons, plants, animals, and soil of North American deserts. Lerner, 2001. [RL 4 IL 4–6] (3434306 HB)

•RL = Reading Level
•IL = Interest Level
Perfection Learning's catalog numbers are included for your ordering convenience. PB indicates paperback. CC indicates Cover Craft. HB indicates hardback.

GLOSSARY

annual (AN you uhl) plant that only lives up to one year

bulb (buhlb) part of a plant found underground from which a new plant grows every year

burrow (BER oh) to dig a hole in the ground for shelter (verb); hole in the ground where an animal lives (noun)

camouflage (KAM uh flahzh) protection due to coloring or behavior that helps an animal blend in with its environment

dam (dam) barrier built across a river to control the flow of water

dormant (DOR muhnt) not growing or developing; inactive

estivate (ES tuh vayt) to go into a deep sleep during hot weather

fiber (FEYE ber) thread used to make cloth or other materials

grub (gruhb) immature form of many insects, especially beetles

habitat (HAB i tat) place where a plant or animal lives

hydroelectric (heye droh ee LEK trik) made by using water to create electricity

irrigation (ear uh GAY shuhn) system for bringing water to a dry area, especially for farming

mesa (MAY suh) flat, high area with steep sides; also known as a butte (byout)

nocturnal (nahk TER nuhl) active at night rather than during the day

organism (OR guh niz uhm) living thing

perennial (per EN ee uhl) plant that lives for more than two years

photosynthesis (foh toh SIN thuh sis) process by which plants use energy from the Sun and carbon dioxide from the air to make food

predator (PRED uh ter) animal that hunts other animals for food

prey (pray) animal that is hunted by other animals for food

reproduction (ree pruh DUK shuhn) process of making more organisms of the same kind (see separate entry for *organism*)

rodent (ROH duhnt) small gnawing animal, such as a mouse or squirrel

sand dune (sand doon) mound or ridge of sand formed by wind or water

transpiration (trans per AY shuhn) the evaporation of water from plants

INDEX